A Tribute to...
NAT KING COLE

IMP

International
MUSIC
Publications

Production: Miranda Steel
Cover Design: xheight design limited
Published 1999

Let There Be Love

Words by Ian Murray Seafield
Music by Lionel Rand

Let there be   you,   let there be   me,

Let there__ be

Let's Face The Music And Dance

Words and Music by Irving Berlin

Let's Fall In Love

Words and Music by
Harold Arlen and Ted Koehler

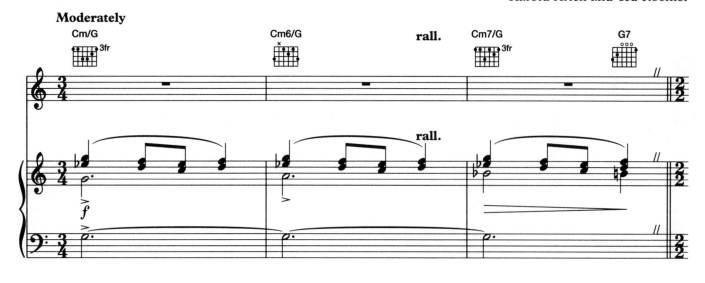

I have a feel-ing, it's a feel-ing I'm con-ceal-ing, I don't know why.
Love fails you ne-ver, his en-deav-our is for-ev-er fate to de-fy,

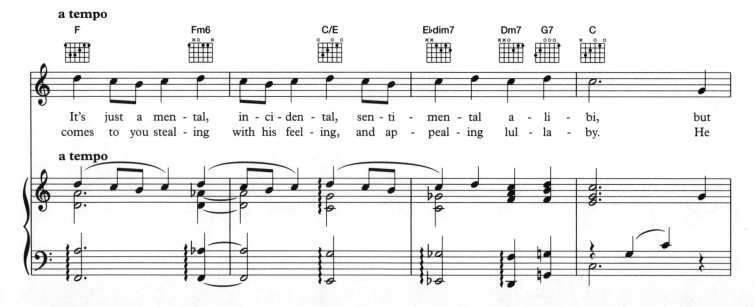

It's just a men-tal, in-ci-den-tal, sen-ti-men-tal a-li-bi, but
comes to you steal-ing with his feel-ing, and ap-peal-ing lul-la-by. He

Love

Words and Music by
Bert Kaempfert and Milt Gabler

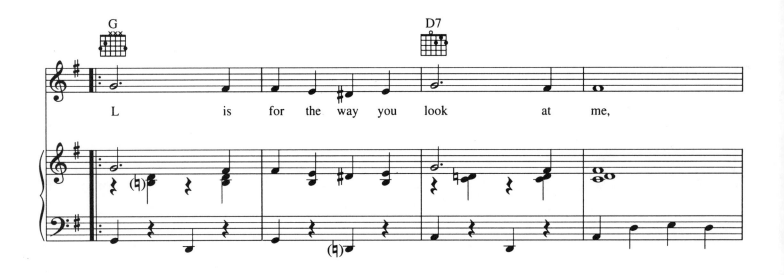

L is for the way you look at me,

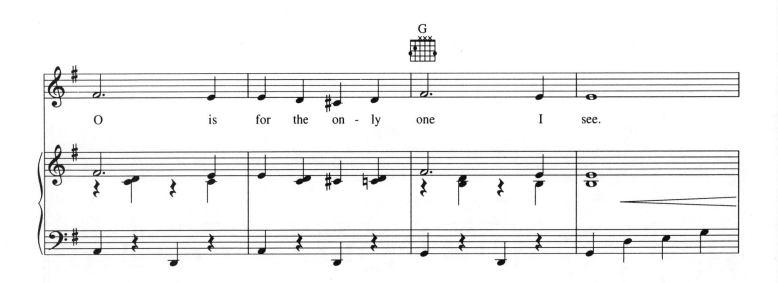

O is for the on - ly one I see.

Two   in love can make it,   take my heart and   please don't break it,

love   was made for me and   you._____

you._____ (That's al - most   true._____) For me and

you._____

Autumn Leaves

Original Words by Jacques Prevert
English Words by Johnny Mercer
Music by Joseph Kosma

Love Is A Many Splendoured Thing

Words by Paul Francis Webster
Music by Sammy Fain

gold - en crown that makes a man a king.

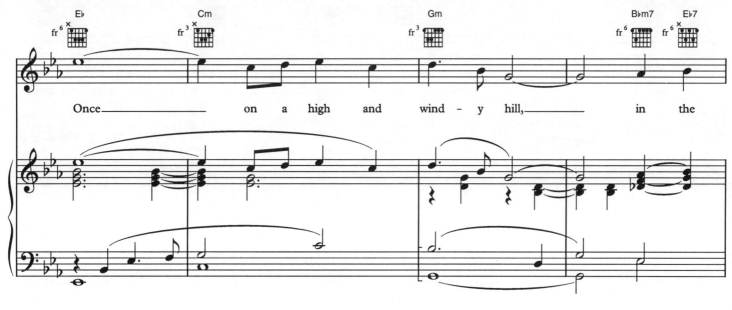

Once_____ on a high and wind - y hill,_____ in the

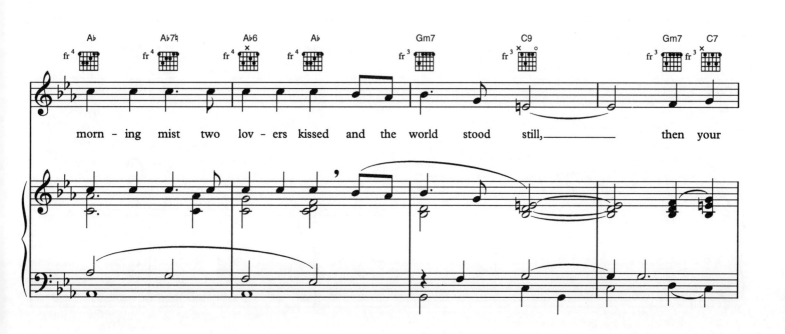

morn - ing mist two lov - ers kissed and the world stood still,_____ then your

Mona Lisa

Words and Music by
Jay Livingston and Ray Evans

In a vil - la in a lit - tle old I - ta - lian town,

lives a girl whose beau - ty shames the rose.

Ma - ny yearn to love her, but their

A Nightingale Sang In Berkeley Square

Words by Eric Maschwitz
Music by Manning Sherwin

On The Street Where You Live

Words by Alan Jay Lerner
Music by Frederick Loewe

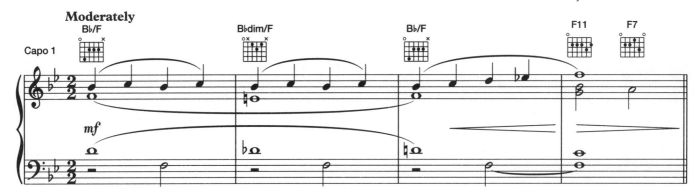

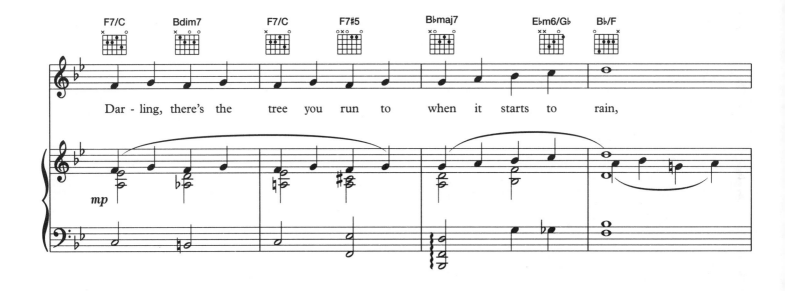

Dar - ling, there's the tree you run to when it starts to rain,

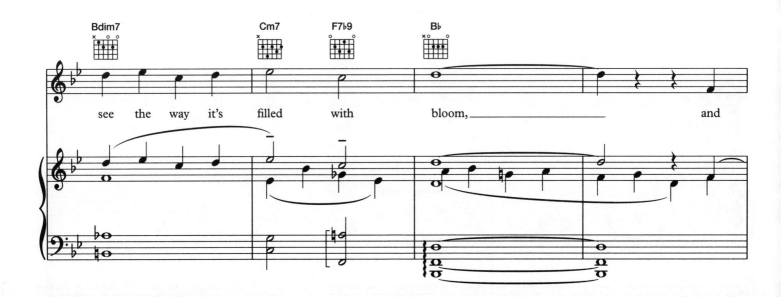

see the way it's filled with bloom, _____ and

Route 66

Words and Music by Bobby Troup

go thro' Saint Lou-is and Jop-lin, Mis-sour-i and Ok-la-ho-ma Ci-ty is might-

-ty pret-ty; you'll see____ A-ma-ril-lo;____ Gal-lup, New

Mex-i-co;____ Flag-staff, A-ri-zo-na; don't for-get Wi-no-na,

King-man, Bar-stow, San Ber-nar-di-no. Won't you____ get hip

Star Dust

Words by Mitchell Paris
Music by Hoagy Carmichael

Unforgettable

Words and Music by Irving Gordon

Love Letters

Words by Edward Heyman
Music by Victor Young

When I Fall In Love

Words by Edward Heyman
Music by Victor Young

sun. When I give my heart, it will be com-plete-ly,

or I'll ne--ver give my heart,_____ and the mo-ment I can

feel that you feel that way too, is when I fall in love with

1.
you._____

2.
you._____

The Very Thought Of You

Words and Music by Ray Noble

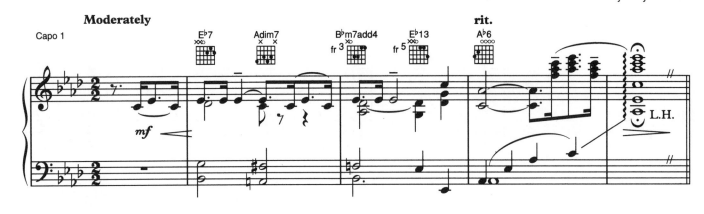

I don't need your pho-to-graph,_____ to keep__ by my bed;
I hold you re-spon-si-ble,_____ I'll take__ it to law,

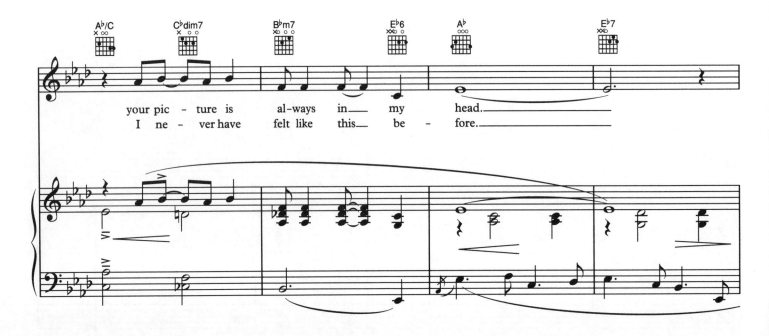

your pic - ture is al-ways in my head._____
I ne - ver have felt like this__ be - fore._____